# Princess Puzzles

Stella Maidment and Daniela Dogliani

QEB Publishing

If you get stuck, the answers are in the back of the book!

This edition published by Scholastic Inc.,
557 Broadway, New York, NY 10012
by arrangement with Quarto publishing.

Scholastic and associated logos are trademarks
and/or registered trademarks of Scholastic Inc.

Distributed by Scholastic Canada Ltd., Markham, Ontario
Scholastic UK, Coventry, Warwickshire
Grolier International, Inc., Makati City, Philippines

Copyright © QEB Publishing, Inc. 2012

First published in the United States by
QEB Publishing, Inc.
3 Wrigley, Suite A
Irvine, CA 92618

www.qed-publishing.co.uk

Editor: Alexandra Koken
Designer: Elaine Wilkinson

A CIP record for this book is available from the
Library of Congress.

ISBN 978-0-545-59009-9

Printed in Guangdong, China

# Welcome to the Palace!

This is the king.

This is the queen.

This is Princess Pearl!

Solve the puzzles in this book and help Pearl find a friend.

Look out for Alphonso the cat, too. You'll find him in every picture!

Princess Pearl lives in a very big palace.

She's in her bedroom in the tallest tower. Can you find her?

Can you spot these things?

two horses

three white birds

a flag

Pearl's playroom is full of toys and games.

Can you spot these things?

two dinosaurs

a drum

a pink rabbit

Can you find
four differences
between the two
teddy bears?

Pearl's dressing room is full
of beautiful clothes.

Can you match her shoes
to her dresses?

Can you spot
these things?

a blue necklace

a golden
chair

a crown

There are lots of lovely things to do in the palace backyard.

Can you spot these things?

a glove

a scooter

a sled

# Can you help Pearl find her way to the swing?

There's just one thing missing:
Pearl has no one to play with!

One of the baby swans is different
from the others. Which one?

Can you spot these things?

three
yellow berries

two
statues

a frog

On Pearl's birthday, the king and queen give her lots of presents.

Can you spot these things?

a blue and yellow present

a book

two birthday cards

Follow Pearl's ribbon to find her favorite present.

Pearl still wishes she had a friend to play with.

Then she notices a door she has never seen before.

Can you spot these things?

three paintings

a suit of armor

a mouse

The door is small and green. Can you find it?

Pearl opens the door and sees some stairs. They lead to the palace kitchen!

Can you spot these things?

an ironing board

a crate of apples

three lamps

Help Pearl find
her way there.

Tilly, the cook's daughter, is helping to make Pearl's birthday cake.

Can you spot these things?

a kettle

two baskets

a clock

Can you find the outlines of a knife, a fork, and a spoon hidden in this picture?

Pearl puts on a striped apron and joins in. Baking is lots of fun!

Can you see three more striped things?

Can you spot these things?

a recipe book

a loaf of bread

butter

Afterward,
Tilly and Pearl play
with Pearl's new
puppet theater.

Can you spot
these things?

three
red
stars

three
puppets

a toy
panda

Can you guess what their show is called?

Pearl has found a friend at last!
"This is my best birthday ever!"
she says.

HAPPY

Can you spot
these things?

Alphonso's
new friend!

three pink
cupcakes

red jello

# Answers

## Pages 4-5

Pearl is circled in red.

## Pages 6-7

The four differences are circled in red.

## Pages 8-9

Follow the lines to match up the shoes and dresses.

## Pages 10-11

Follow the red line to the swing.

## Pages 12-13

The baby swan circled in red looks different.

## Pages 14-15

Pearl's ribbon (highlighted in red) leads to the puppet theater.

## Pages 16-17

The small green door is circled in red.

## Pages 18-19

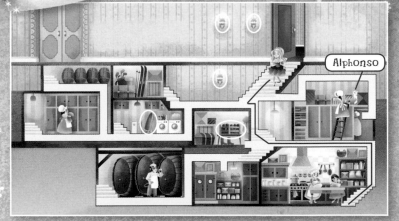

Follow the red line to the palace kitchen.

# Answers

Pages 20-21

The three outlines are circled in red.

Pages 22-23

The three other striped things are circled in red.

Pages 24-25

The show is called "Little Red Riding Hood."

Pages 26-27

The matching balloons are circled in red.

# More Princess Fun

## Princess Day
Dress up like a princess for the day! Put on a pretty dress and see if you can borrow some necklaces or bracelets to wear. Use a towel for a cloak and tape or safety pin it to your dress. You could even have a princess-themed party!

## Put On A Show!
You can put on a puppet show just like Pearl and Tilly! Cut out pictures of people or animals from magazines and stick them on the ends of chopsticks, wooden spoons, or popsicle sticks. Hide behind a couch and hold your puppets up so they peek over the top. Then, let the puppet show begin!

## Make A Jeweled Crown
Find a strip of colored paper that's long enough to wrap around your head. Then, cut a zigzag edge along the top. To make "jewels," cut out circles or diamonds from foil or cellophane wrappers. Now glue the shapes onto the crown to decorate it. When you are finished, glue or tape the ends of the crown together.

## Make A Royal Castle
Draw an outline of a castle on a piece of paper. Use paints, crayons, or pencils to color it in. Then, draw a king, a queen, and a princess on separate pieces of paper. Cut them out and glue them onto your castle. When you've finished, you can hang your castle picture on the wall!